Girls

2000

stickers

Puzzly, pretty, cutesy, and doodly!

PARRAGON

Bath • New York • Singapore • Hong Kong • Cologne • Delhi
Melbourne • Amsterdam • Johannesburg • Shenzhen

Kittens!

Which little kitten has unraveled the knitting?

A

B

C

D

How to draw a kitten ...

1

2

3

Match each kitten with its bed.

Just like this one!

Fluff Balls

Turn these cuddly balls into cats and kittens!

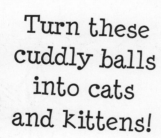  

Kitty Fact:
Kittens begin dreaming when they are just over 1 week old!

Add your own beautiful charms to these bracelets.

Then color them all
in pretty colors!

It's **busy** at this horse riding school!

Use your stickers to show what the
horses and their riders are doing.

Splash!

These mermaids love spending lazy summer afternoons at the enchanted lagoon.

Can you find eight differences between these two pictures?

Color a shell as you find each one.

Fishy Faces

Create some little ocean creatures by adding faces to these shapes.

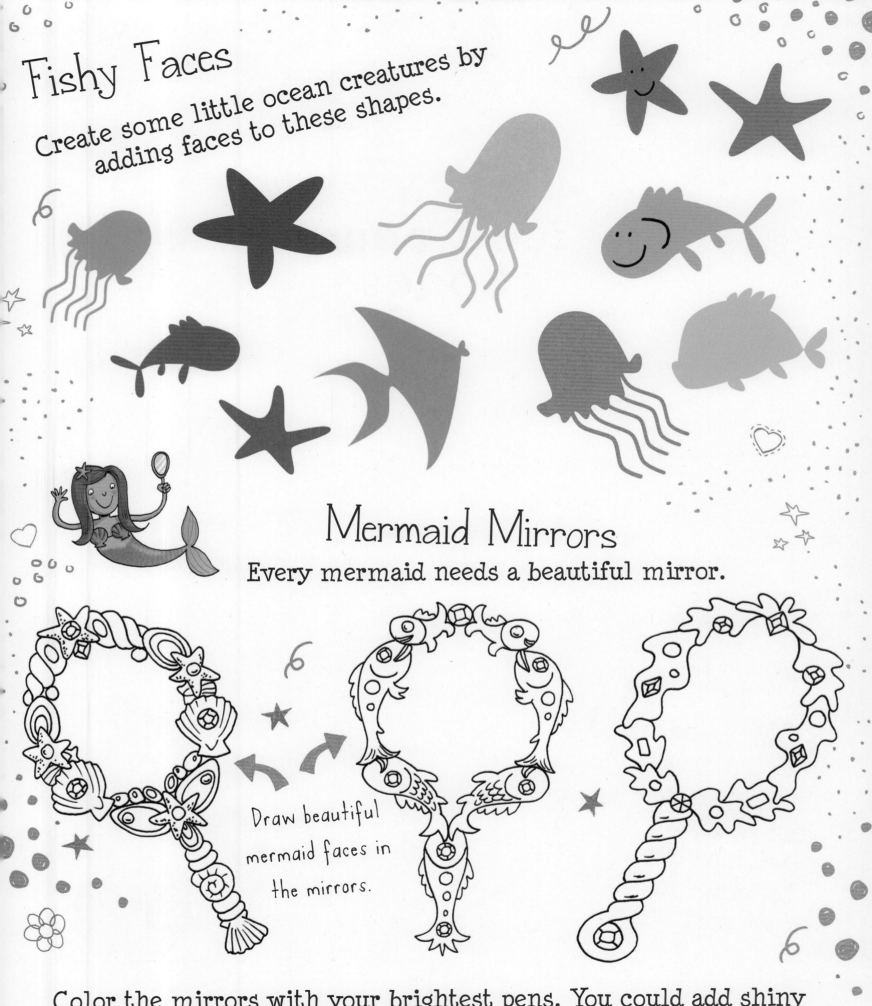

Mermaid Mirrors

Every mermaid needs a beautiful mirror.

Draw beautiful mermaid faces in the mirrors.

Color the mirrors with your brightest pens. You could add shiny paper, sequins, or glitter to make them shimmer in the sunlight.

Ice-Cream Cones

YUM! Doodle a big ice-cream in this glass and decorate it with swirly toppings and sweet sprinkles.

Draw some scoops of ice-cream
on these ice-cream cones.

Who Lives Here?
Use your stickers to add more
furniture and the dolls to this house.

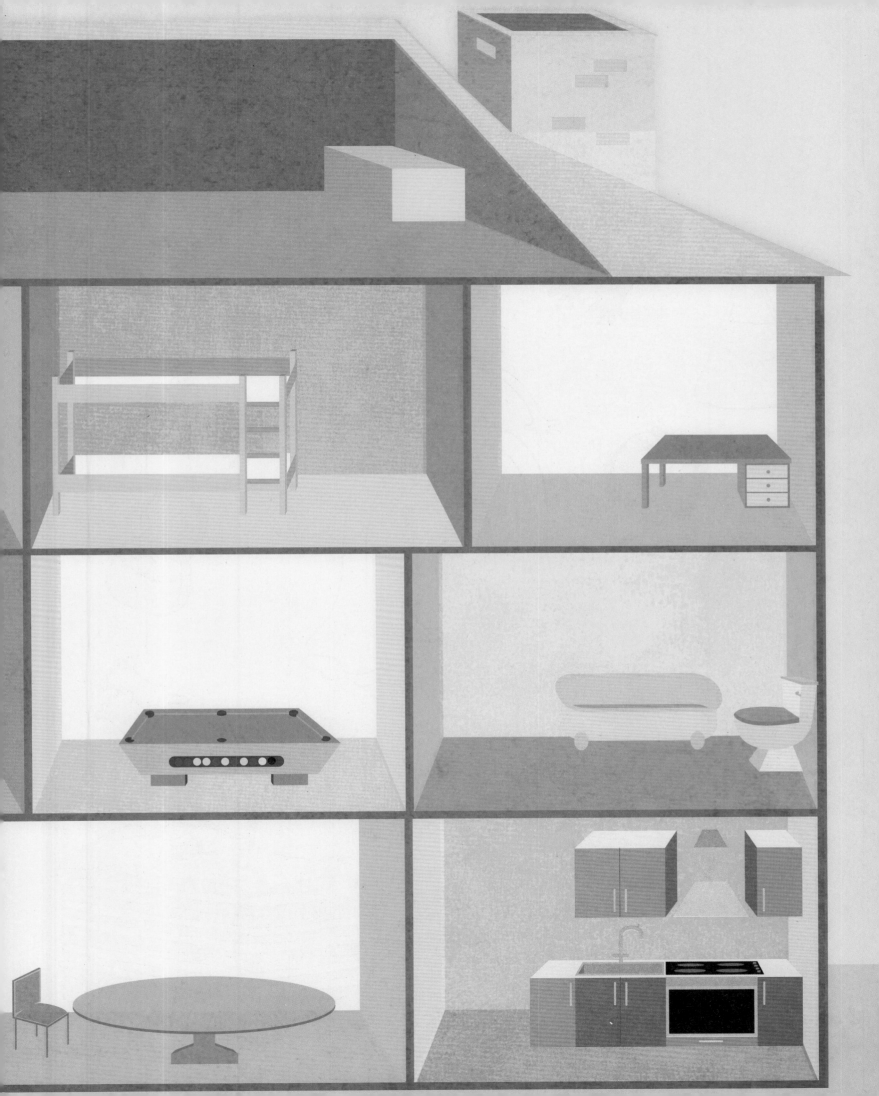

Perfect Princess

Belle of the Ball

Princess Polly is going to a Summer Ball at the Prince's palace tonight.

Help her choose shoes, a tiara, jewels, and a handbag, then color in the dress to match.

Princess Slumbers

How many mattresses does the princess have on her bed?

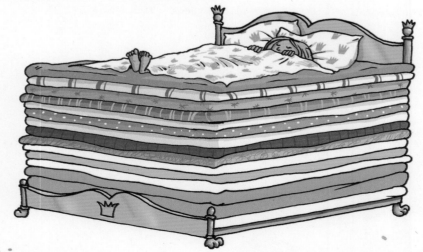

Princess Poppy is late for the ball! Which route will take her to her carriage and horses?

A

B

C

The Frog Prince

Princess Isabella must kiss one of these frogs in the palace pond to turn it into a handsome prince.

But which frog should she kiss?

Fill the sky with
hot air balloons.

Up, up, and away!

It's **party** time!

Use your stickers to show everyone having fun at this birthday party—don't forget to add lots of yummy treats!

Ponies!

Draw a circle around each thing Hattie needs to go horse back riding.

Saddle Up!

Penny's pony doesn't like the water jumps!
Can you show Penny a way through the show jumping
course that avoids all the water jumps?

Finish

Start

Color in these cute ponies.
Give them each a beautiful mane and a special name.

Spot five differences between these two show jumping horses.
Color a rosette for each one that you find. When you have
found them all, color the winner's trophy!

Funny Faces

Finish off these faces so they all look different.

Draw a big smile on this one.

YAWN!
Make this one
look sleepy.

The **stage** is **set** ...

now add the ballet dancers putting on a magical show!

This cute puppy is lost.
Help him find his way home
through the maze.

Love Hearts

Color in these cute hearts then doodle lots of your own!

Looking fabulous!

Use your stickers to add the stylish outfits these catwalk models are wearing.

Cloudy Picture

Turn these clouds into people or animals.

Pack the Picnic!

Circle all the things that need to be packed into the picnic basket.

Fluttering Butterflies

Color in the patterns on these butterflies.
Can you find the matching pair?

Flowers

Draw some more flowers in the park, and add some bugs crawling and flying around them.

Add wings, feelers, faces, and legs to these fingerprint bugs!

Fun at the Fair!

Use your stickers to show all the people
busy enjoying themselves at the fairground.

Double Trouble

Can you find three differences between these twins?

Color a box for each one you find.

Now, decorate their outfits!

Did you know?
Animals (including cats, dogs, and sheep) can be twins, too!

Summer Time!

Draw two more flowers in these pots and color them in.

Can you see three butterflies in the garden?

Trace the outline to draw the bird's house.

Swoosh! Splash! Quack!
This animal sanctuary is
packed with animals!

Use your stickers to show
all the mischief and
mayhem they are causing!

Magic Fairies!

Help this fairy through the forest to find her friend.

Start

Finish

How many fairies have a wand with a star on?

Which two of these fairies have the same pattern on their wings?

There are all kinds
of **canine capers**
at this dog show!

Use your stickers to show
what the dogs are doing.

Answers

Which little kitten has unraveled the knitting?

Match each kitten with its bed.

Can you find eight differences between these two pictures?

How many mattresses does the princess have on her bed?
 15

Princess Poppy is late for the ball! Which route will take her to her carriage and horses?
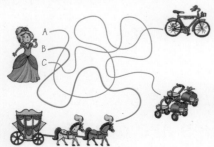

Princess Isabella must kiss the frog prince by the fountain to turn it into a handsome prince.

Draw a circle around each thing Hattie needs to go horseback riding.

Penny's pony doesn't like the water jumps! Can you show Penny a way through the show jumping course that avoids all the water jumps?

Spot five differences between these two show jumping horses.

Draw lines to match each poodle to its shadow.

Help the puppy find his way home through the maze.
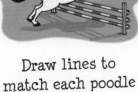

Circle all the things that need to be packed into the picnic basket.

Can you find the matching pair?

Can you find three differences between these twins?

Help this fairy through the forest to find her friend.

How many fairies have a wand with a star on? 2

Which two of these fairies have the same pattern on their wings?